Mothers & Daughters
A Record Book About Us

havoc

PUBLISHING

© 1997 Havoc Publishing

ISBN 1-57977-111-4

Published and created by Havoc Publishing

San Diego, California

First Printing, August 1997

Designed by Juddesign

Printed in China

Please write to us for more information on our

Havoc Publishing Record Books and Products.

HAVOC PUBLISHING

6330 Nancy Ridge Drive, Suite 104

San Diego, California 92121

Mothers & Daughters

A Record Book About Us

&

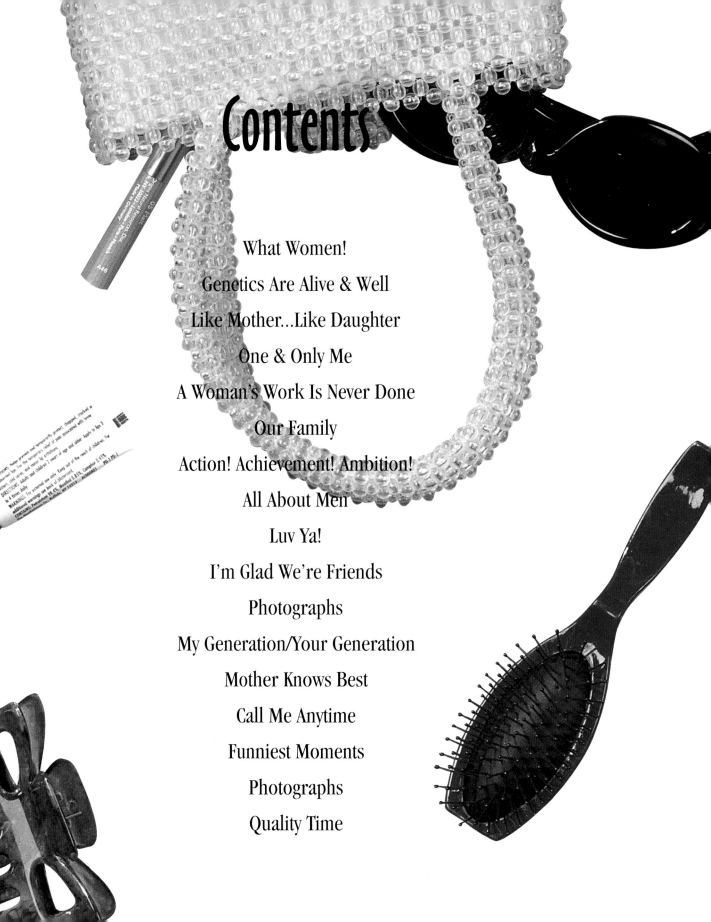

Contents

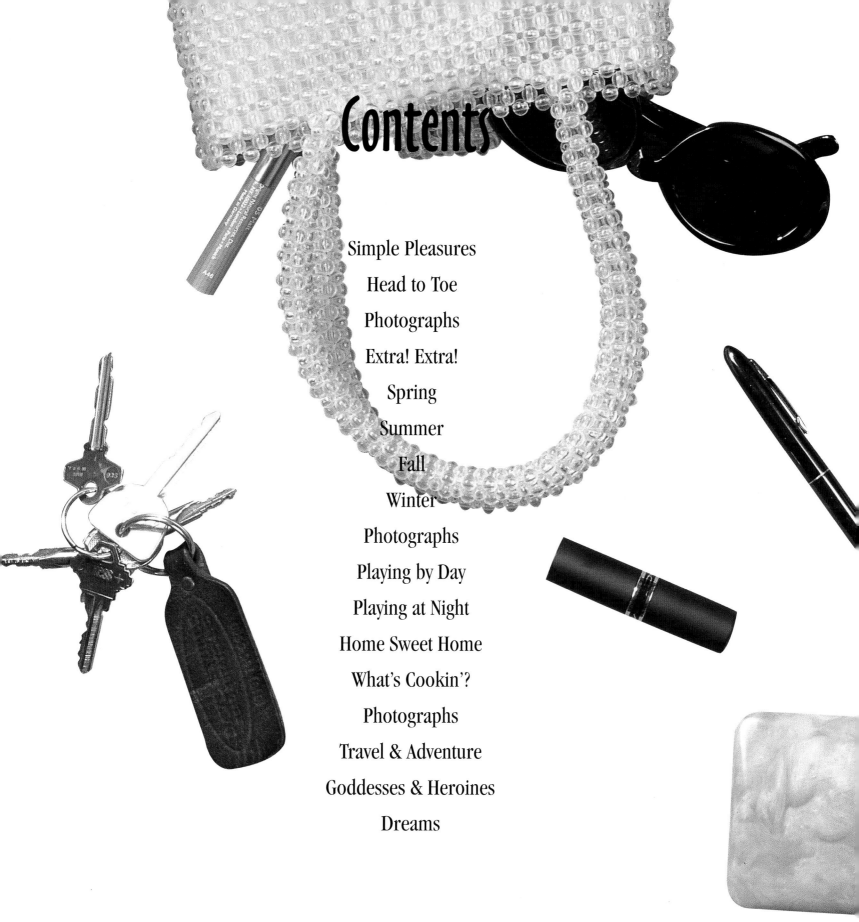

Contents

What Women!

A photo of the two of us

Birth date

Birth date

Birth place

Birth place

Address

Address

Other pertinent information

Other pertinent information

Genetics Are Alive & Well

Mother

Hair

Eyes

Height

Skin tone

Other features

Ways we are alike

Daughter

Hair

Eyes

Height

Skin tone

Other features

Ways we are different

Like Mother...

Photo

...Like Daughter

Photo

The first time I noticed we were like each other

_____
_____
_____
_____
_____

Things you say that I say

_____
_____
_____

Things you do that I do

_____
_____

One & Only Me
(& You)

Things about us that are unconventional

_____

_____

What I think is special about you

_____

_____

Similar interests

_____

_____

Different interests

_____

_____

Photo

A Woman's Work Is Never Done

Photo

My traditional roles

❑
❑
❑
❑
❑
❑
❑
❑

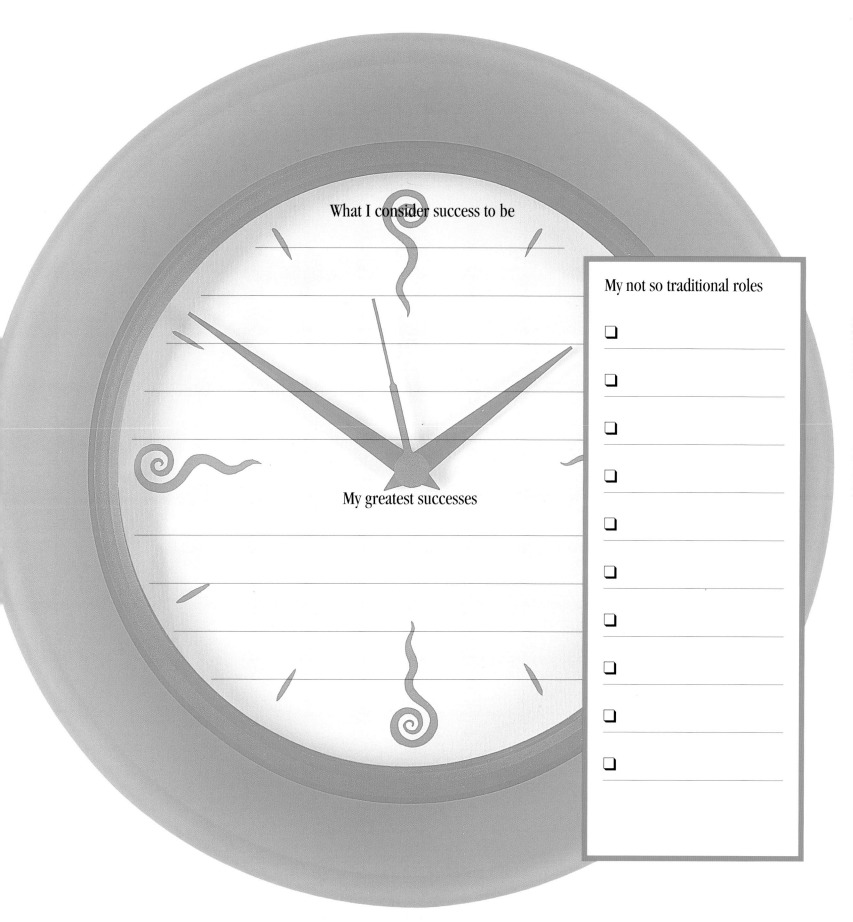

What I consider success to be

My greatest successes

My not so traditional roles

❑
❑
❑
❑
❑
❑
❑
❑
❑
❑

Our Family

Family get-togethers, celebrations & birthdays

_____

_____

_____

_____

_____

Traditions

_____

_____

_____

_____

Name

Relationship

Birth date

Name

Relationship

Birth date

Name

Relationship

Birth date

Name

Relationship

Birth date

Name

Relationship

Birth date

Name

Relationship

Birth date

Home Sweet Home

My Home

_____

What makes it special

_____

_____

My decorating style

_____

_____

Projects still to be done

_____

_____

_____

Photo

Your Home

_____

What makes it special

_____

_____

_____

The best household tips you've given me

_____

_____

_____

Photo

Action! Achievement! Ambition!

My greatest achievements are

I think your greatest
achievements are

My proudest moment
with you was

Award Certificate

This award is presented to

_____

for

_____

_____
signed

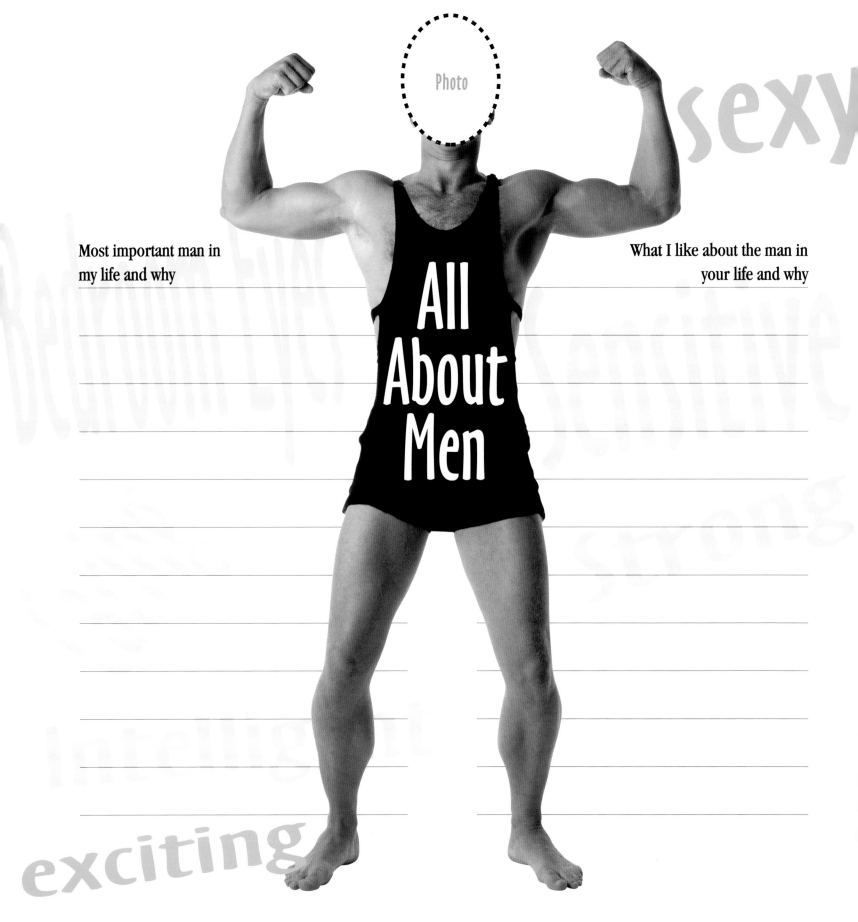

Photo

Most important man in
my life and why

What I like about the man in
your life and why

All
About
Men

"A woman without a man is like a fish without a bicycle"
— Gloria Steinem

Heroes and men I admire

_____

_____

_____

_____

Best advice you have given me on men

_____

_____

_____

Things you've taught me about men

_____

_____

_____

_____

_____

_____

_____

_____

_____

Luv Ya!

What I love most about you

_____

_____

_____

_____

_____

_____

_____

_____

Photo

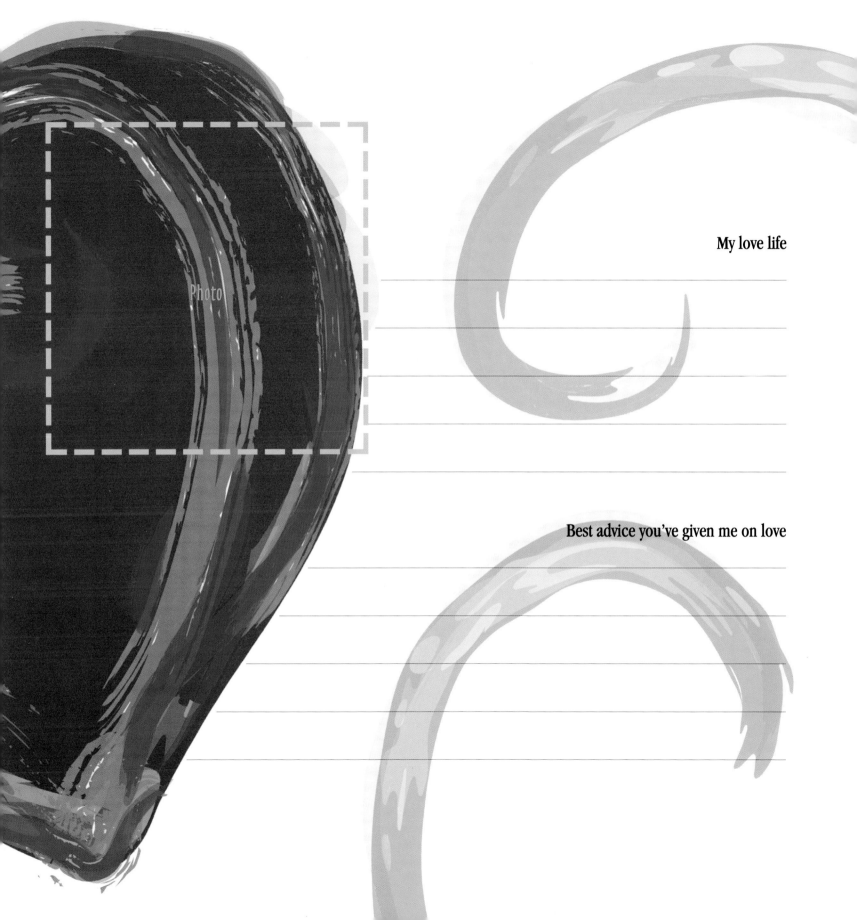

Photo

My love life

_____

_____

_____

_____

_____

Best advice you've given me on love

_____

_____

_____

_____

I'm Glad We're Friends

I'm glad we're friends because

Things I'm glad we can share

_____

_____

_____

_____

I love it when we

_____

_____

_____

_____

_____

_____

Photograph

Photograph

My Generation

I love your youthful approach to...

_____

_____

_____

You're so mature about....

_____

_____

_____

Ways I stay young

_____

_____

_____

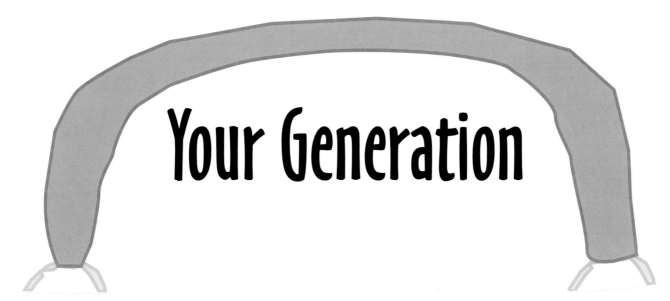

Your Generation

What I like about getting older

_____

_____

_____

What I appreciate now

_____

_____

_____

What I like about your generation

_____

_____

_____

Mother Knows Best

Photo

You mean I never told you about...

I guess it's safe to tell you now...

I can't believe you said that!

What were you thinking

Call Me
Any Time

Funniest Moments

Things that always make us laugh

Remember laughing about...

Hee! Hee! Hee!

How humor has helped us

_____

_____

_____

_____

_____

_____

_____

_____

Favorite jokes or fun stories

_____

_____

_____

_____

_____

_____

_____

_____

Photograph

Quality Time

Favorite outdoor activities we share

_____

_____

_____

_____

Favorite indoor activities we share

_____

_____

_____

_____

Favorite times we spend together

_____

_____

_____

_____

_____

Favorite malls/shops

_____

_____

_____

Simple Pleasures

Our happiest times

_____

_____

_____

_____

Favorite ways to relax

_____

_____

_____

_____

Photo

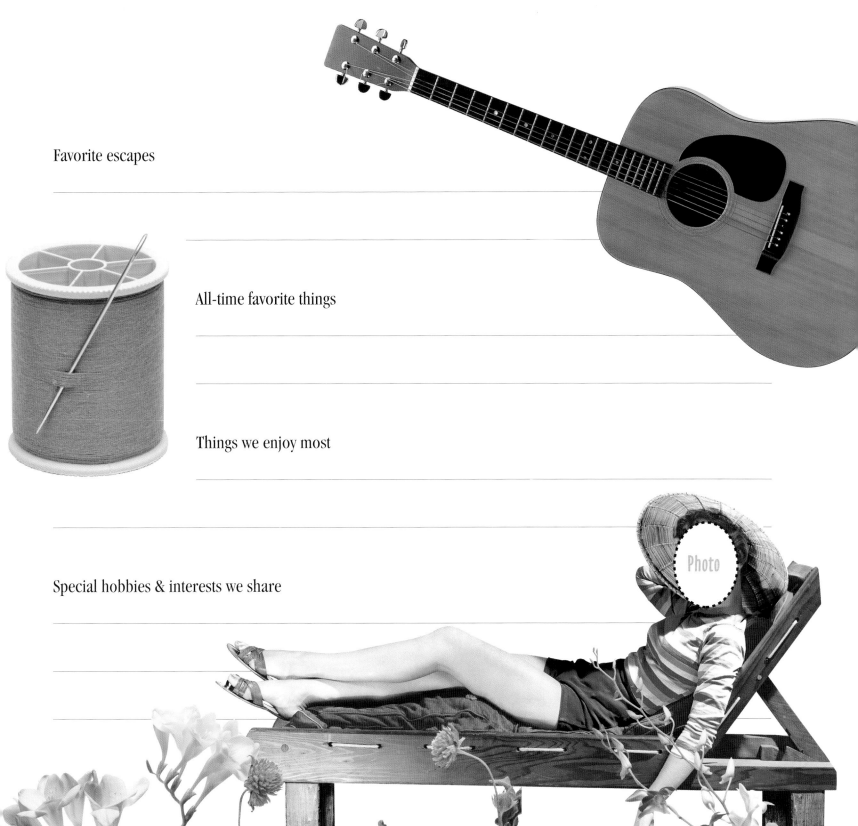

Favorite escapes

All-time favorite things

Things we enjoy most

Special hobbies & interests we share

Head to Toe

Feeding our minds

_____

_____

_____

Pampering

_____

_____

_____

Health & beauty tips

_____

_____

_____

_____

_____

How we keep in shape – physically & mentally

_____

_____

_____

_____

Feeding our bodies

_____

_____

_____

Exercising Health Beauty
Pampering Minds Bodies Relaxing
Exercising Health Beauty
Pampering Minds Bodies Exercising
Health Beauty Pampering
Minds Bodies Relaxing Exercising
Health Beauty Pampering
Minds Bodies Exercising Health
Beauty Pampering Minds
Bodies Relaxing Exercising Health
Beauty Pampering Minds
Bodies Relaxing Exercising Health

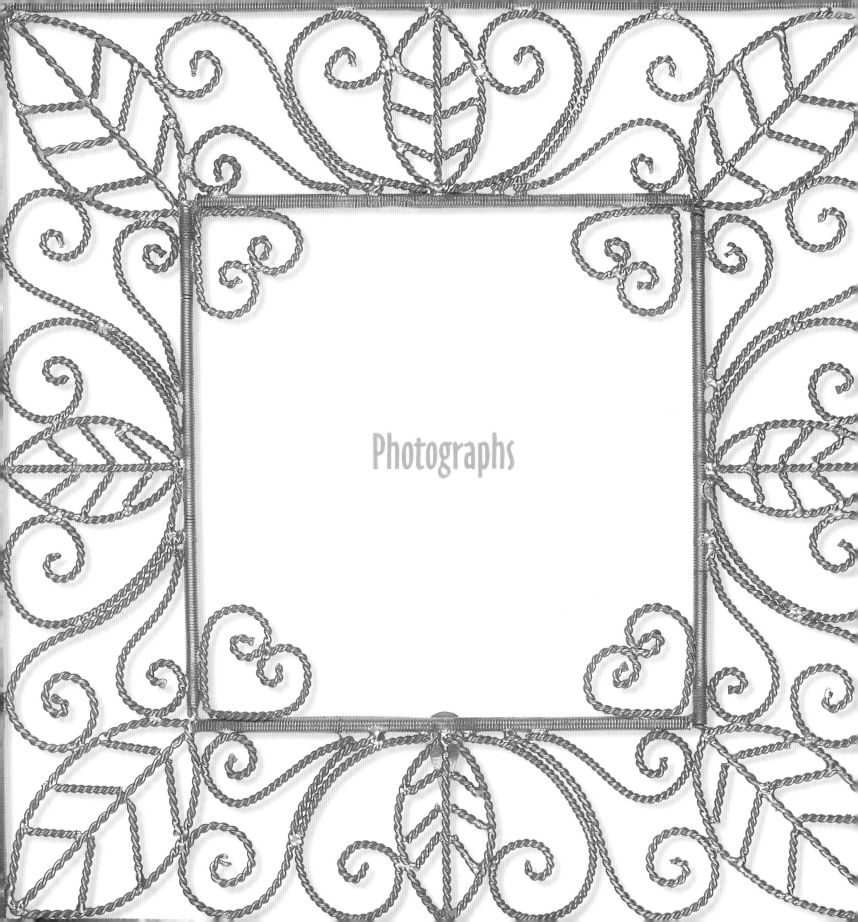

Photographs

Photographs

EXTRA!

How the world has changed

_____

_____

_____

Hot political issues

_____

_____

_____

How my views of the world have changed

_____

_____

_____

EXTRA!

World events that have affected us

Environmental issues

Our favorite things to do in the Spring

_____

_____

_____

_____

_____

Holidays, special events and trips together

_____

_____

_____

Our favorite things to do in the Summer

_____

_____

_____

_____

_____

_____

Holidays, special events and trips together

_____

_____

_____

_____

_____

_____

_____

Our favorite things to do in the Fall

_____

_____

_____

_____

_____

_____

Holidays, special events and trips together

_____

_____

_____

_____

_____

Our favorite things to do in the Winter

_____

_____

_____

_____

_____

_____

Holidays, special events and trips together

_____

_____

_____

_____

Photograph

Photograph

Playing by Day

My favorite way to spend a day with you

_____

_____

_____

_____

_____

_____

_____

_____

Photo

Best evenings
out together

Playing at Night

Photo

What's Cookin'?

Mealtime favorites

Best recipes

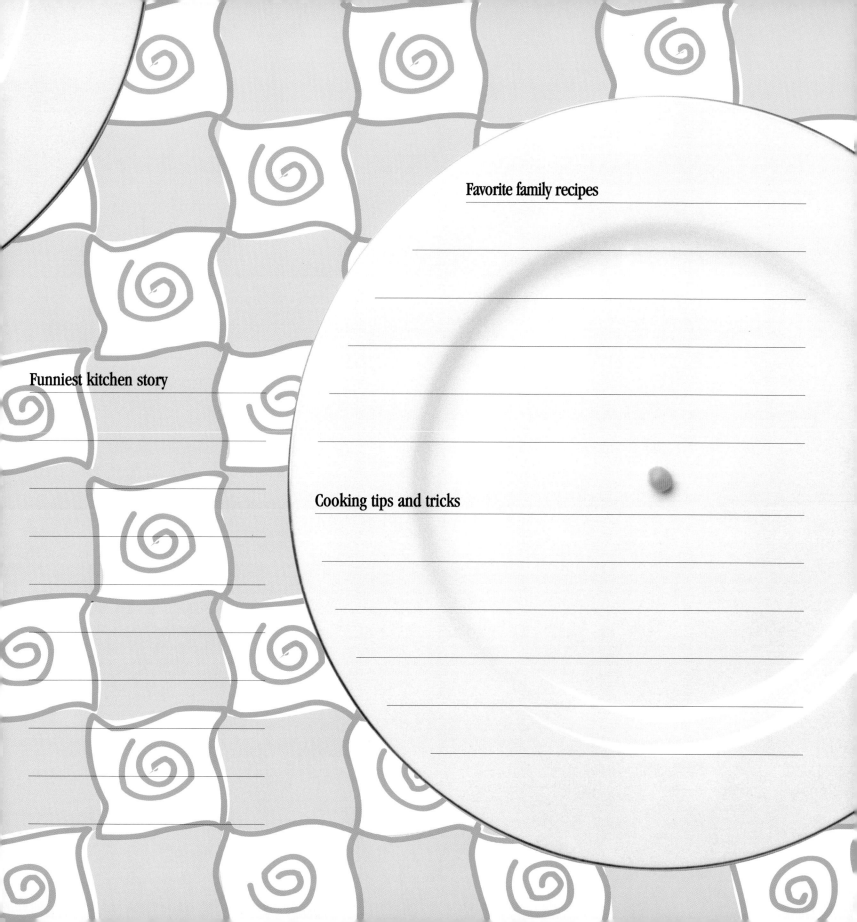

Favorite family recipes
_____
_____
_____
_____
_____

Funniest kitchen story
_____
_____
_____
_____
_____

Cooking tips and tricks
_____
_____
_____
_____

Photographs

Photographs

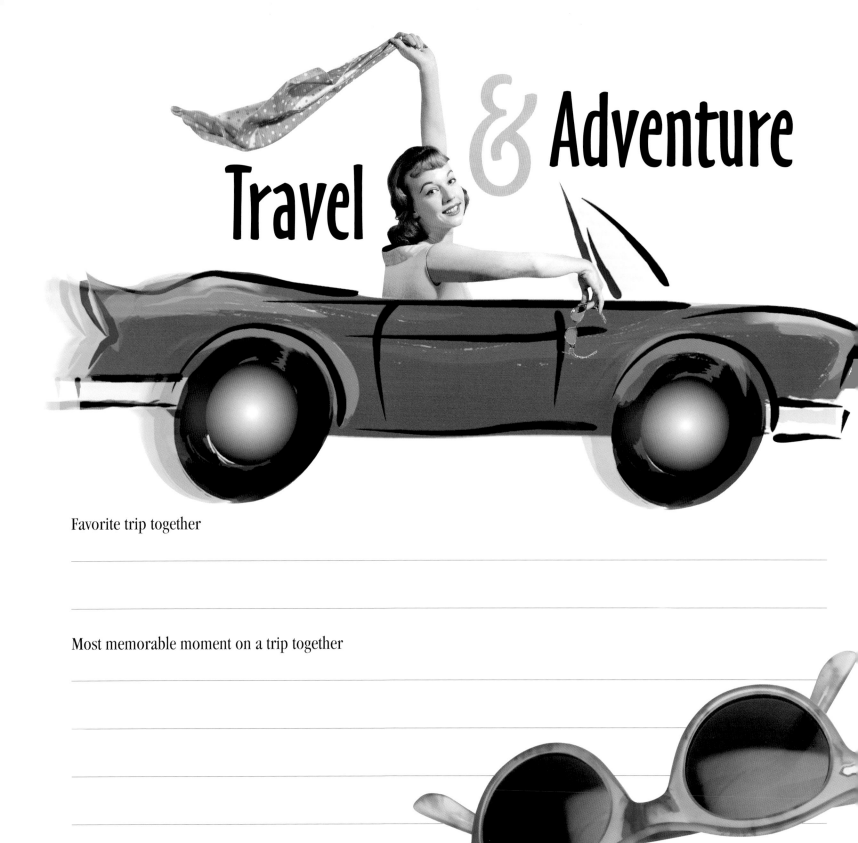

Travel & Adventure

Favorite trip together

Most memorable moment on a trip together

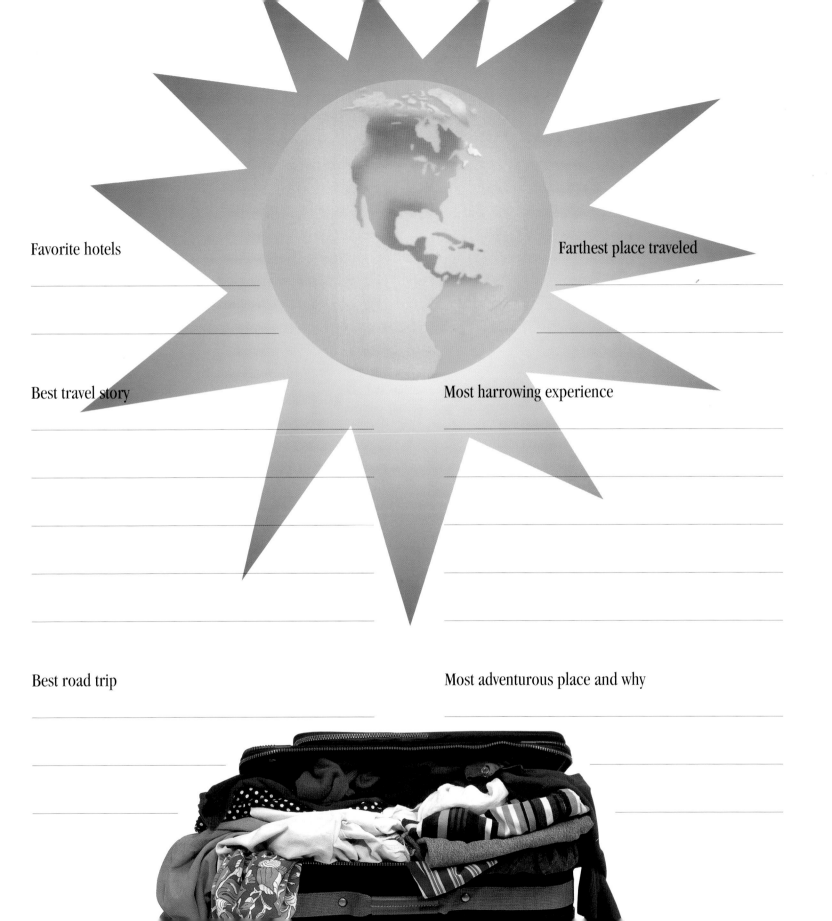

Favorite hotels

_____

_____

Farthest place traveled

_____

_____

Best travel story

_____

_____

_____

_____

Most harrowing experience

_____

_____

_____

_____

Best road trip

_____

_____

_____

Most adventurous place and why

_____

_____

Goddesses & Heroines

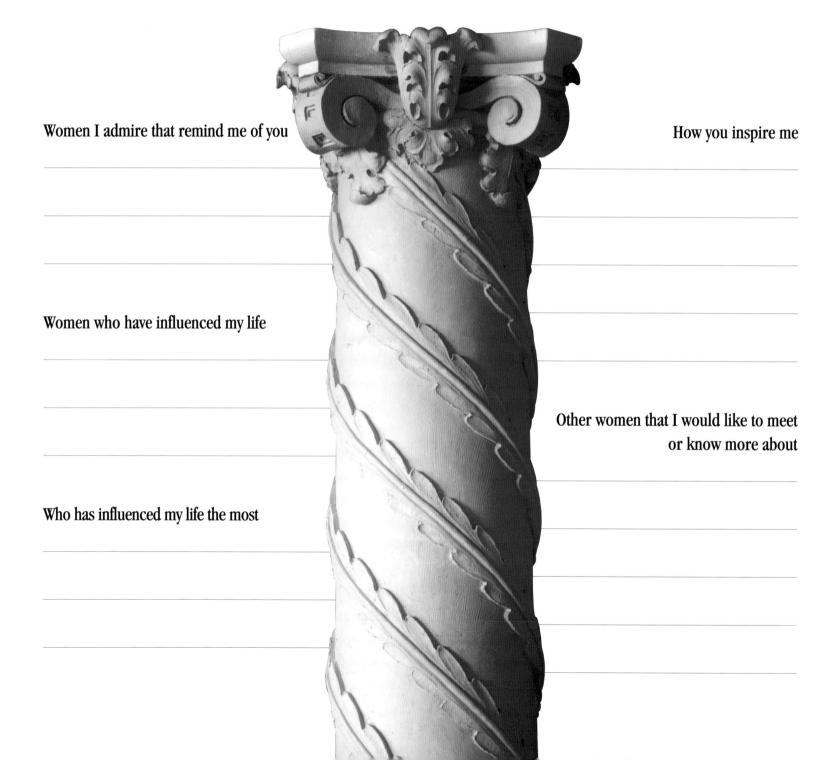

Women I admire that remind me of you

Women who have influenced my life

Who has influenced my life the most

How you inspire me

Other women that I would like to meet
or know more about

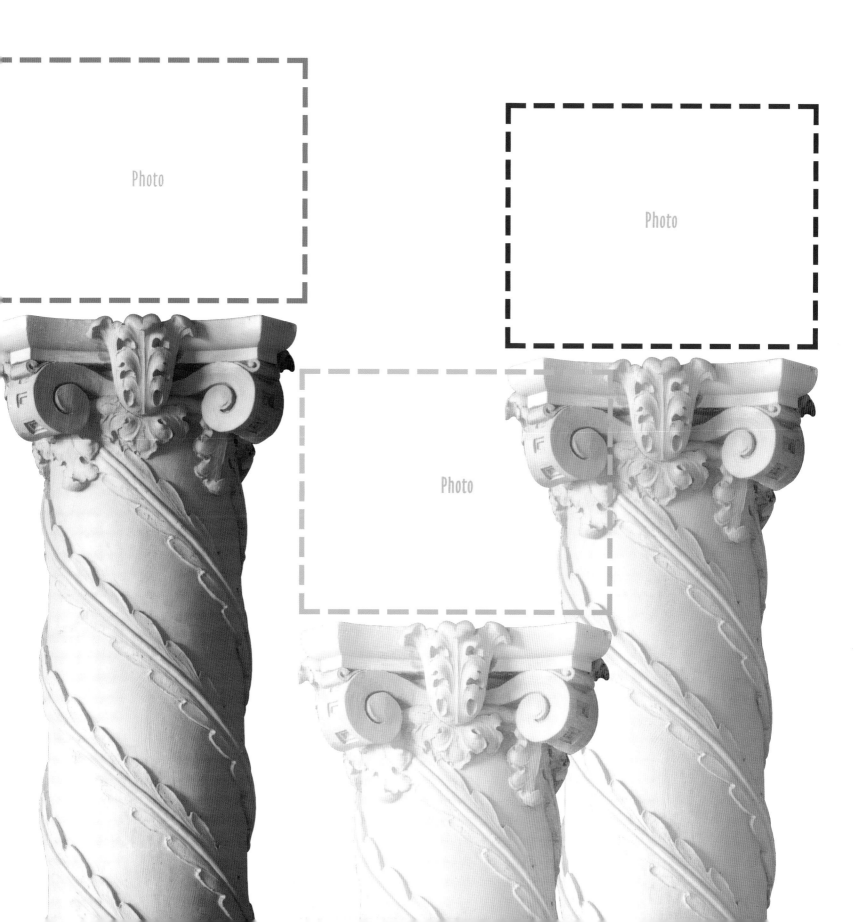

Photo

Photo

Photo

Dreams

For Me

_____

_____

_____

_____

_____

_____

Dreams

For You

_____

_____

_____

_____

_____

_____

Other Available Record Books from Havoc

Animal Antics-Cat

Animal Antics-Dog

Couples

Girlfriends

Golf

Grandmother

Mom

Mothers & Daughters

My Pregnancy

Our Honeymoon

Retirement

Sisters

Teacher

Traveling Adventures

Tying The Knot